Creative Expression

Splash of Color

Coloring Fun for People of All Ages

PUBLISHER
Peter Kanter

SENIOR V.P. SALES
& MARKETING
Bruce W. Sherbow

V.P. DESIGN & PRODUCTION
Susan Mangan

V.P. EDITORIAL
& PRODUCT DEVELOPMENT
Christine Begley

DIRECTOR OF MARKETING,
BRAND LICENSING
& E-COMMERCE
Abigail Browning

READER'S SERVICE
Betty Andrews

CORPORATE SALES
For quantity discounts to
qualifying groups and
organizations contact:
corporatesales
@pennypublications.com

Most images provided by
Shutterstock, Inc.
Cover and additional images
provided by Susan Wygant.

Coloring is a meditative pursuit that can help to relieve your stress and focus your mind. It is a good way to practice mindfulness in our busy, fragmented world. Taking some time out of your hectic day can make you feel calmer and more centered.

If you're new to coloring, check out some of our tips on the opposite page to help you get started. But remember—there are no rules. These are your pictures, to color your way.

Share your #PennyDellColors with us! We would love to see your finished pieces, so tag your works of art with #PennyDellColors on Instagram, Pinterest, Facebook or Twitter.

Please visit us at **PennyDellPuzzles.com**

SPLASH OF COLOR, Volume 3. Published bimonthly by Penny Press, Inc., 6 Prowitt Street, Norwalk, CT 06855-1220. On the web at PennyDellPuzzles.com. Copyright © 2016 by Penny Press, Inc. Penny Press is a trademark registered in the U.S. Patent Office. All rights reserved. No part of this magazine may be reproduced in any form or by any means without the prior written permission of the publisher. We are not responsible for the loss of unsolicited material.

Printed by RR Donnelley, Mattoon, IL U.S.A. 5/2/16

A lovely being, scarcely formed or moulded,
A rose with all its sweetest leaves yet folded.

—Lord Byron, *Don Juan*

Loads of thoughts,
love + care!
Marilyn
(MC)
xoxo

Parents are friends that life gives us;
friends are parents that the heart chooses.

—Comtesse Diane, *Les Glanes de la Vie*

Once I spoke the language of the flowers,
Once I understood each word the caterpillar said,
Once I smiled in secret at the gossip of the starlings,
And shared a conversation with the housefly in my bed.

—Shel Silverstein, *Where the Sidewalk Ends*

There is a sumptuous variety about the New England weather
that compels the stranger's admiration—and regret . . .
In the spring I have counted one hundred and thirty-six
different kinds of weather inside of four-and-twenty hours.

—Mark Twain

Experience shows us that love does not consist in gazing at each other but in looking together in the same direction.

—Antoine de Saint-Exupéry, *Man and His World*

When you take a flower in your hand and really look at it, it's your world for the moment. I want to give that world to someone else. Most people in the city rush around so, they have not time to look at a flower. I want them to see it whether they want to or not.

–Georgia O'Keeffe

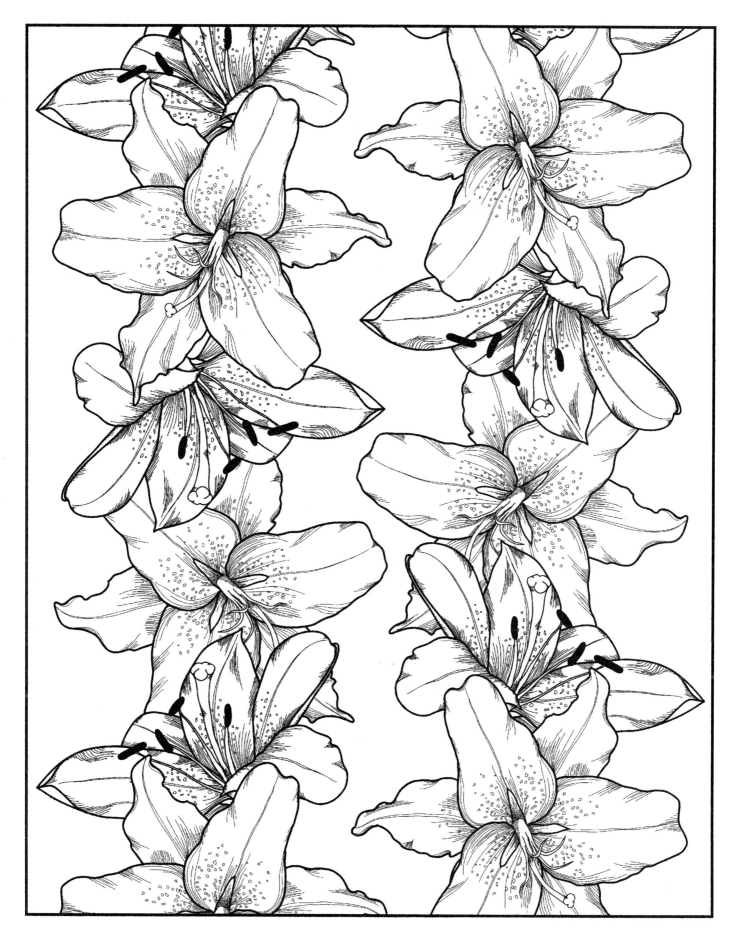

Blessed are those who can give without
remembering, and take without forgetting.

—Elizabeth Bibesco

There's no beginning to the farmer's year,
Only recurrent patterns on a scroll
Unwinding.

—Vita Sackville-West, "Spring"

Farewell to thee, farewell to thee
The charming one who dwells in the shaded bowers
One fond embrace
'Ere I depart
Until we meet again.

— Lili'uokalani, "Aloha Oe"

Love recognizes no barriers. It jumps hurdles, leaps fences, penetrates walls to arrive at its destination full of hope.

–Maya Angelou

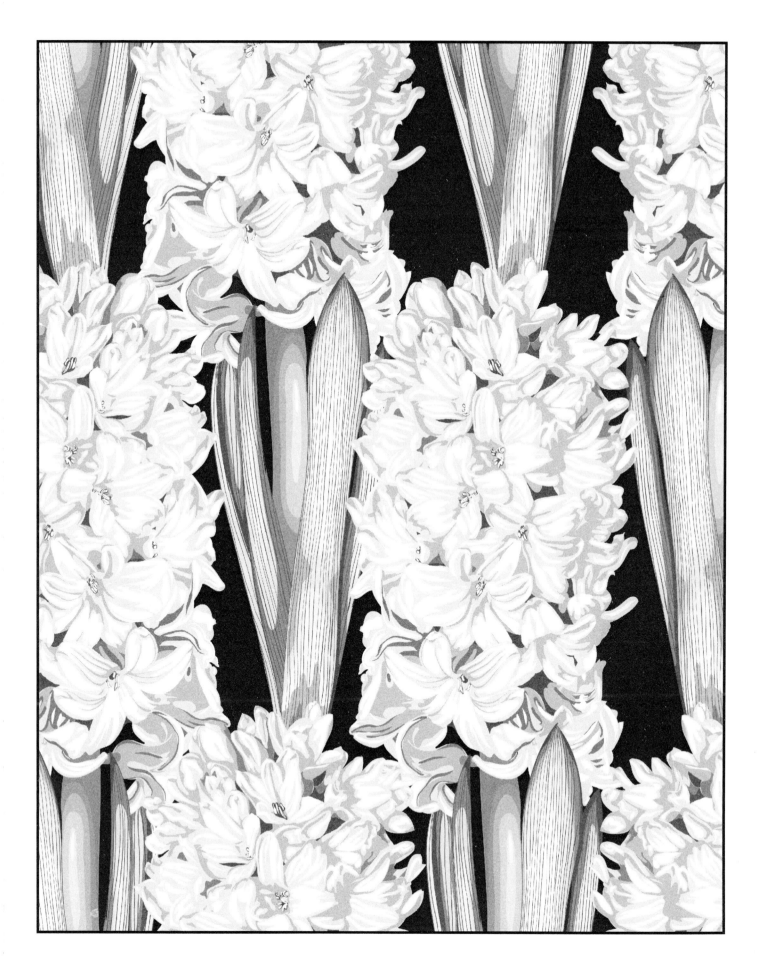

Too much of a good thing can be wonderful.

—Mae West, *Goodness Had Nothing to Do With It!*

Friendship's a noble name, 'tis love refined.

–Susan Centlivre, *The Stolen Heiress*

The fragrance always remains in
the hand that gives the rose.

—Heda Bejar

Charm is the ability to make someone else
think that both of you are pretty wonderful.

—Kathleen Winsor, *Star Money*

Nobody has ever measured, even the poets,
how much a heart can hold.

–Zelda Fitzgerald

A cheerful giver does not count the cost of what he gives. His heart is set on pleasing and cheering him to whom the gift is given.

—Julian of Norwich, *Revelations of Divine Love*

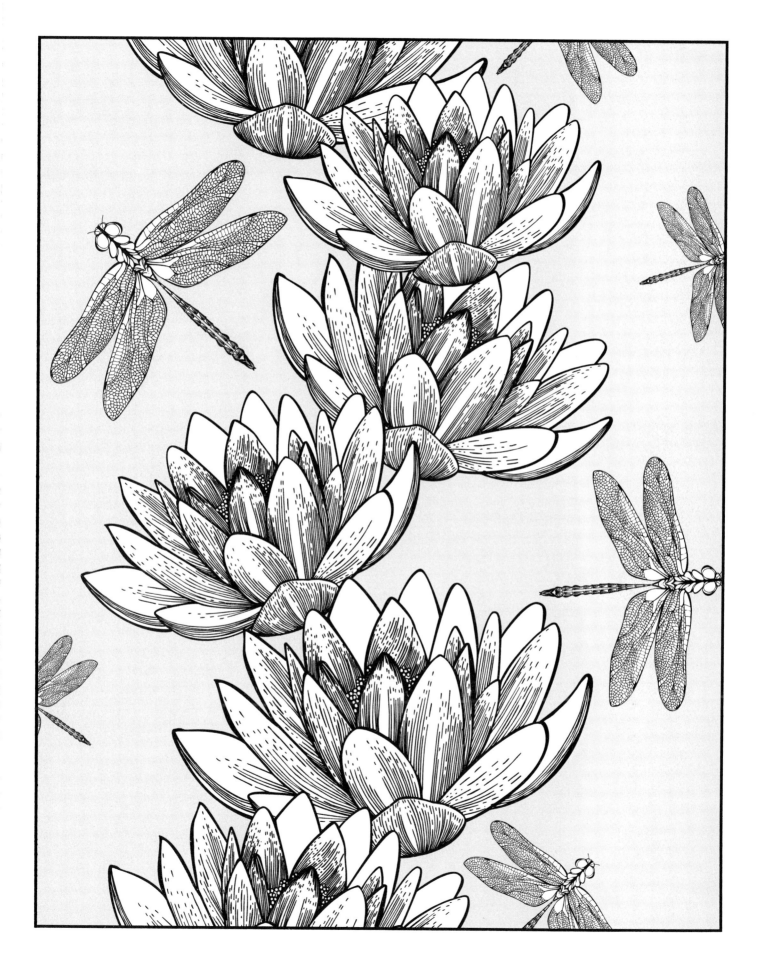

Rose is a rose is a rose is a rose.

—Gertrude Stein, *Sacred Emily*

She believed in excess. How can you tell whether or not you have had enough until you've had a little too much?

—Jessamyn West, *Hide and Seek*

Fill the cup of happiness for others, and there will be enough overflowing to fill yours to the brim.

—Rose Pastor Stokes

Shall I compare thee to a summer's day?
Thou art more lovely and more temperate:
Rough winds do shake the darling buds of May,
And summer's lease hath all too short a date.

—William Shakespeare, Sonnet 18

Earth laughs in flowers.

—Ralph Waldo Emerson, "Hamatreya"

One violet is as sweet as an acre of them.

—Mary Webb, *The Spring of Joy*

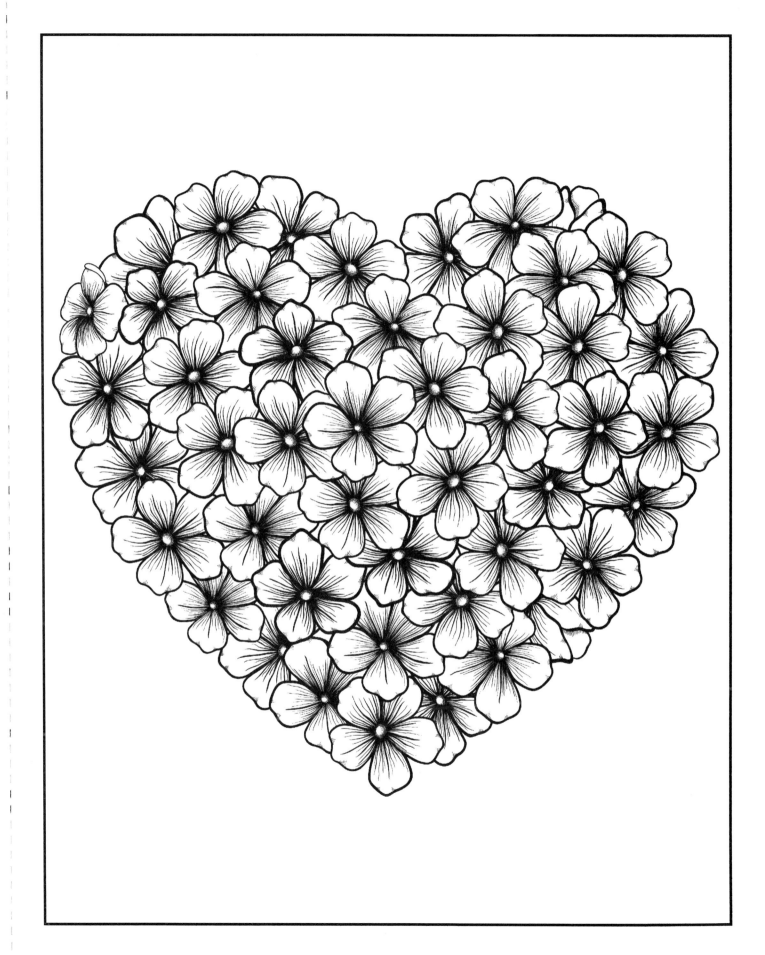

It seems to me that trying to live without friends is like milking a bear to get cream for your morning coffee. It is a whole lot of trouble, and then not worth much after you get it.

—Zora Neale Hurston, *Dust Tracks on a Road*

Daisy, Daisy, give me your answer do!
I'm half crazy, all for the love of you;
It won't be a stylish marriage,
I can't afford a carriage
But you'll look sweet upon the seat,
Of a bicycle made for two!

—Harry Dacre, "Daisy Bell"

One could not live without delicacy, but when
I think of love I think of the big, clumsy-looking
hands of my grandmother, each knuckle a knob.

—Mona Van Duyn, "A Bouquet of Zinnias"

Flowers and plants are silent presences;
they nourish every sense except the ear.

—May Sarton, *Plant Dreaming Deep*

Apology is a lovely perfume; it can transform
the clumsiest moment into a gracious gift.

—Margaret Lee Runbeck, *Time for Each Other*

Abundance is, in large part, an attitude.

—Susan Patton Theole, *The Woman's Book of Confidence*

O, my Luve's like a red, red rose
That's newly sprung in June;
O my Luve's like the melodie
That's sweetly play'd in tune.

—Robert Burns, "A Red Red Rose"

The secret of a happy marriage is finding the right person. You know they're right if you love to be with them all the time.

–Julia Child

Happiness often sneaks in through a door
you didn't know you left open.

–John Barrymore

Enough is as good as a feast.

—Katharine Tynan, *The Years of the Shadow*